DNA OF A CUCKOLD - ADVANCED COUPLES EDITION

The Next Level; When You Both Embrace Your Place And How You Want To Live

ALLORA SINCLAIR

DNA Of A Cuckold - Advanced Couples Edition

©2021 by Allora Sinclair

The publisher and the author make no guarantees concerning the level of success you may experience by following the advice and strategies contained in this book, and you accept the risk that results will differ for each individual. The testimonials and examples provided in this book show exceptional results, which may not apply to the average reader, and are not intended to represent or guarantee that you will achieve the same or similar results. It is meant as a source of valuable information for the reader, however it is not meant as a substitute for direct expert assistance. If such level of assistance is required, the services of a competent professional should be sought.

Front Cover Illustration by: Stylepics

To Anthony and Michael. You have brought me to levels of ecstasy that I thought not possible. Your deep understanding and kind guidance have only made my love for davie and my commitment to the lifestyle even deeper. I love you guys xo.

WHY YOU SHOULD NOT READ THIS BOOK

What an odd title for the first chapter of a book. I did this because I want to caution any couples not fully established in a cuckolding relationship. There is far too much-distorted information about this lifestyle loaded with flagrant lies. If you were to believe any of it, you would think that a husband can "make" his wife become a hotwife/cuckoldress (YOU CAN NOT), or that a cuckol-dress can "manipulate" her husband into being her little bitch boy (YOU CAN NOT DO THAT EITHER).

As I've mentioned in my previous two books, cuck-olding is not something you just simply do. Perhaps a hotwife set-up, where it's just about the sex, this may be the case, but cuckolding goes beyond the bedroom. It's an all-encompassing way of life by two mutually consenting adults.

The catch is this mutual consent must come from the heart, not the head. Agreeing to be cucked or to have sex with other men in front of your husband is only one small part of the overall equation.

This advanced user's guide is NOT for anyone who feels at their core that this lifestyle is just for fun. Don't get me wrong, it's a ton of fun. But the true cuckold and cuckoldress do this because it is part of who they are. They do it because it completes them as a person. It closes their internal loop of how their ideal life should go.

Yes, a lot of psycho mumbo jumbo there. The point is if you do not need to be cuckolded, or have a need to be sadistic, this book will only make things go south with your relationship. Therefore, I want to caution all readers, the content beyond this introduction is not for wannabes or newbies. It is exclusive to cuckolding couples that are completely comfortable being the way they are and now want even more.

It took davie and I a good two years before we stopped fighting with our internal conflicts. Over 30 years of being programmed by a society that you need to behave in a certain way, takes some time to deprogram. Though not all the material ahead will be extreme, a large portion magnifies the real core of the cuckold dynamic to levels that will not align with the part-time cucks.

I have broken this book into three separate sections so issues can be found easily as couples travel this deeper level of the lifestyle. Part I looks at the plethora of fun activities you can get up to, to accentuate sexual pleasure once the novelty of sex outside the marriage is over. Part II dives deeper into more extreme forms of disparity, humiliation and control. In a nutshell, stuff that now probably appeals to you, but did not when you were first coming to terms with cuckolding. Part III examines the struggles cuckold couples face that no one talks about. How do we deal with the kids? Do we tell them? Ongoing issues of imbalanced and un-agreed disparity and the dreaded fear of losing the love balance within the relationship.

I have tried very hard to create a step-by-step series that will help couples in this lifestyle. I have also tried to present things in an open and honest fashion tempered with big warning signs of caution to all those 'just curious'. I feel morally obligated to downplay many of the amazing aspects of cuckolding because it has the real potential to end marriages. You can not be in this life safely if your DNA is outside its parameters.

Every word on every page has been thought through and reviewed by both davie and myself. I got the idea of creating this series because we were so sick of the lies. We both came across many sources that presented cuckolding information that was exclusively designed to turn the reader/viewer/listener on, take their money, and not give a shit about the sanctity of their marriage.

I say all this because, from this point forward, I would consider the topics discussed reckless to those not completely immersed in the lifestyle already. To us, it has become our little piece of heaven.

Chapter One

CHASTITY

*I*nevitably, chastity will come up as a topic of conversation. Read any book on cuckolding, female-led relationships or S&M, this is usually the go-to starting point beyond all things sex. Why do you think this is the case?

CONTROL. Control is the number one reason any couple would use any form of a chastity device. Often referred to as a cock cage, this is a lockable device that is placed over the cuck's penis, secured (usually) by employing an additional wrap-around style piece that prevents it from being removed without the cuck's balls being destroyed. The good ones are extremely effective and comfortable to wear for long periods. They range around $50 but can be more or less expensive if you shop around. Davie finds the metal ones are easier to get on and off, allow for hygiene better and are more secure. Problem.

They weigh a little more and can become uncomfortable when I have him wearing one for extended periods.

I have put chastity as the first topic because this is a must-do if any actual progress is to be made in accentuating the cuckold experience. It ensures that your cuck remains celibate at all times, without your knowledge and approval. The longer a man goes without releasing his 'wisdom', the more compliant he becomes. I don't want to pretend to know the science behind the male anatomy but trust me, it is sooo true. One of the later troubleshooting topics I discuss stems from this. I have become so used to having davie wrapped up that I rarely want to let him have an orgasm for fear he will change his approach to our lifestyle. When I allow him to release, I always make sure it's on the days just before we have our 'day off'.

The other bonus to a cock cage is, let's face it, it's humiliating. I love when we are out and davie needs to use a public washroom. The uncomfortable moments he feels standing at the urinal must be hilarious. I know he has not only come to expect it; he loves it. Bottom line, if you're not already using chastity, do it. Do it now. You can thank me by giving this book an excellent review.

Finally, there is the question of when and for how long? This is a very individual answer. You are a couple that loves each other. Having an orgasm is a biological need, not a want. The ridiculous stories I've heard of guys being locked up for months at a time I doubt are true. It's certainly not healthy for his prostate. The goal is to have him caged as much and as long as humanly possible, BUT not to the point of being downright cruel and unhealthy.

I have davie locked up no more than two weeks at a time, but often it's for only several days. Once I've had some playtime with one of my bulls, I know he's ready to blow. Rarely do I deprive him of this joy, but I also lock him back up the second he shows any signs of angst. It is the perfect cure for my sad puppy dog when he feels sorry for himself.

Chapter Two

TOYS, TOYS, TOYS

✻

*D*ildos, vibrators, strap-ons, a Sybian. Oh my. The fun you can have here. This may seem like it does not differ from a vanilla relationship. How wrong you would be. Toys in a cuckold relationship are not so much about pleasing the female, but rather, about REPLACING your cucky as the primary source of pleasure when it's just the two of you.

I'm assuming you already have a collection of toys accumulated from the days when you were exploring the idea of cuckolding. Now I'm suggesting you take them to a new level with more items added to the toy shopping cart. The dildo that you used while he watched. Now he's the one using them.

What? Yes, that's correct. Now he's an active player using the vibrator and dildo on you. The catch? This becomes IN LIEU of him serving you directly. It's a winning set-up for both of you. Assuming you have purchased wisely, your dildo will surely be bigger and more ridged than his little pee pee. The vibrator, well, that's just special for any occasion. The arrangements need to change so that now; he uses these toys on you rather than you on yourself.

Though very expensive (over $1200 USD), getting a Sybian (an actual motorized unit that is straddled) does all the work for both of you. He can sit and watch as you get off by a machine. They're loud, but my God, they're effective. The only thing either of you needs to do is plug it in and set the control dial for speed and intensity.

The point is not to see your toys as an added way for pleasure, they also should play with the cuckold mind. Every single time toys are used instead of your cuckold using his own body, it sends a small message. It puts his equipment out of service not just with other men, but also when it's just the two of you.

Yes, this can be seen as cruel and unfair, but that's kind of the point. Same as chastity. If it's overdone, then it's abusive and not cool. You need to balance all the dynamics to ensure there is disparity, selfishness and humiliation. But only up to where it is welcomed. This will be an ongoing theme throughout the balance of this book. If it's working for you, use it. Maybe even consider more of it. Just be careful to remember the why.

Strap-ons I have left to last. This can be where things get too extreme for davie and I. That being said, I get. I'd love to try it, but my princess is only willing to strap it on himself to fuck me instead of his real pee pee. He has made a hard line that he is not interested in having me 'man-up' and strap it on to have my way with him. I get it.

It's the ultimate domination move a woman can make,

but sadly, he's a bit of a homophobe. For some couples, this is an amazing experience. Prostate stimulation on a male can make a regular orgasm seem lame. I would love the control and domination to fuck the shit out of my little davie. I think he'd love it. For now, it is a line he has asked I respect. I encourage you to take the same approach with each other at all times.

Chapter Three

IS MY DINNER READY?

⚶

uckolding is seriously underrated for all the other wonderful perks that come with it beyond the sex. Once you've crossed the bridge, and openly had sex outside the marriage, there can be a long adjustment period. It was a huge hurdle: you both had to jump, and then jump again, and so on.

As the novelty wears off, you will both look for ways to maintain that rush you had from the first time. Because it was all new to both of you. The mere act of knowing she's going to openly suck another man's cock, or that he has become so encouraging and compliant. It's a massive euphoric feeling that I swear is addictive. The early stages need little to make you both feel the power and control or the humiliation and deprivation. We both still talk about that first time, like it happened last week.

The evolution of this disparity will inevitably spill over to the household. The cuck needs to feel useful in other ways. He craves it. The need to be controlled is an aphrodisiac to him. The cuckoldress loves loves LOVES the power. So why are you sharing the daily chores I ask? Because that's what you've always done as a couple? Did you always have an open marriage?

Things have changed, large. It's in line with supporting your mutual end goal to look for innocent ways to accentuate the disparity even more. It can be very easy to overlook this side of cuckolding or conversely, take things too far where love gets blurry and hostility breeds.

I know, I know. I sound like a broken record, but you need to discuss things on 'off days' to establish how much work you want to take on or how many chores you want to unload. As the cuckold, you may feel overwhelmed at the prospect of taking on the cooking, or maybe you would love to do her laundry so you can get up close and personal to your goddess's dirty panties? As the cuckoldress, you may still love cooking and don't see it as a chore. Delegating this to your cuck would then be counterproductive to your end goal.

What is the end goal?

Cuckoldress = Goddess, Queen Bee, The Absolute Center of the Cuck's Universe

Cuckold = A tiny man that is lucky to have such an amazing Goddess

Everything that you can both do to magnify the above is a step in the right direction. The more unfairness, the happier you both naturally feel. Remember, this is no one's fault. Cuckolding does not look to justify or explain or judge. You love each other at such an intense level BECAUSE it is this way.

The more work cucky princess can take on, the better.

If he is eager to do everything, let him. If your cuckoldress has piled too much on, you need to vocalize this on your 'days off'.

The less work around the house you have to concern yourself with, the better. However, don't delegate if it's something you enjoy (cooking for some). If your objections to have cucky do things are because you're very particular, then take the time to teach him to do things exactly the way you like them done. Be careful not to be over aggressive in handing out tasks. Cucky will do anything you ask of him, even if it does nothing for him. Check-in on this during your weekly 'check-in days' to ensure you have not overburdened him.

Chapter Four

HEY, PRINCESS

ow many times have you heard a wife call her husband "princess"? Maybe you've heard her call him "hun" or "babe" or even "sweetie". But princess? As you progress in your cuckold relationship, you both will begin to feel more and more comfortable in your respective roles. As the cuck, you stop fighting the belief that you need to preserve your manhood as dictated by society. You accept the role of cuckold in a more all-encompassing way, beyond your wife's sexual escapades. As a cuckoldress, you too will feel less and less guilty about your actions. You'll see that the more you act like a goddess, the more you're treated like one and expect to be treated like one.

For the cuck, humiliation, particularly PUBLIC humiliation, can be a game-changer. You're both out shopping. No sex is on the discussion table. You turn to your cuck and speak to him loud enough that the guy with a shopping cart close by can hear you. You so innocently say "princess, go get me some cat food". You both leave a restaurant and stand outside to have a cigarette. Your goddess throws the butt on the ground, extinguishes it with her high heels, and then tells you to "pick it up and place it in the garbage receptacle" while three others stand there and watch.

These are just a couple of examples of what public humiliation can mean. It does not mean you have to cause a scene. Nor does it have to be over the top degradation. Each couple has their routines. I'm suggesting that you build in constant little actions that will cause a degree of humiliation. It helps maintain the headspace of sadism and masochism.

I like to think of it as little cock teases. Humiliating your cuck publicly will probably get him a little hard. Being an obedient little boy to his goddess will create and reinforce the message that she has you completely wrapped around her finger, just the way you like it.

If you're both reading this book as a couple, I encourage you to stop and openly discuss this point. You may not even be aware that your partner would appreciate these insignificant gestures. They are completely non-sexual actions that, to a cuckold couple, accentuates the experience dramatically. It may surprise you how effective it is for both of you when you return home.

This all being said, humiliation, particularly PUBLIC humiliation, can be a very slippery slope if it's overdone or done without commitment. It needs to happen. You both want it to happen. It will happen. Just be careful.

If your cuckoldress calls you a stupid princess and you're with your colleagues from work, this may be too much. You must live with this humiliation well beyond your wife's comment in your workplace. If your neighbor asks to borrow some sugar and you insist your cuck answers the door wearing the lovely silk panties you want him to wear in the house, you could have an incredibly awkward relationship with them going forward.

Have fun with it. Learn when and when not to do it. Make sure you understand each other's comfort zones and respect them at all times. The longer you live in this lifestyle, the more comfortable you both become with this kind of thing, but it also can cause you both to become insensitive to your partner's boundaries.

Chapter Five

SUN, SURF AND NAILS

✦

*A*s a cuckoldress, if you haven't already started moving in this direction, I would ask "What the hell are you waiting for"? This is one area that I was like a duck in water. I did not need any lessons or provocation. You are only limited by the amount of discretionary income you have.

Your little cuck worships you. I think we've beaten this one to death. So, in his eyes, you are a goddess that can truly do no wrong. The more you act and think of yourself as his goddess, the more he will appreciate it.

Where the money comes from, we will discuss in the next section, but for now, let's assume you no longer need to be 'responsible'. Do you want a new $400 hairstyle? Those sexy red sole Louboutin stilettos? A vacation to that resort that only offers sun and sand and no golf? Do it. Do it all! Being selfish as a cuckoldress is not just allowed, cucky prefers it. The more, the better.

I swear to God, I have seen davie get hard every time I tell him "no, you can't buy that new tool for work". Meanwhile, I will have just come back from the tanning and nail salon. Remember, disparity is your best friend. Don't believe me? Try it.

Vanity for the cuckoldress is a key component of the cuckold mind. He loves to see his wife looking good. Knowing she is spending his money to look good for other men is when it becomes a game-changer. That deep tan, those sexy nails, that skimpy outfit. Even better, that breast enlargement. They're for Tom? I can hear his pants stretching already.

Again, these are all little steps that davie and I have taken outside the bedroom that bring our cuckolding relationship to extra levels. Being a bitch is something I was told was always looked down upon. I love being a bitch. I don't have to work at it. It just comes naturally to me. Here's the magic. Davie loves it too. The more I take and the less I give, the better. This is not just with what gets done around the house. It also goes with where the money is spent, on who and for what.

As the saying goes; 'all work, and no play makes Jack a dull boy'. This is true. Never allowing your cuck to have the odd indulgence is over the top. He needs to have some fun, some treats. There needs to be some temperance. If he really needs that tool to do his job properly, then obviously spend the money and get it.

My point is, this should only be done sparingly. A flagrant imbalance of who gets spoiled should always remain intact. But not when it sucks all the fun out of life or causes bankruptcy.

One last point on this. ANYTHING you do as a

cuckold to make your cuckoldress feel guilty or question her judgment can prove fatal down the road. Trust that she has your best interest at heart. If you feel the imbalance is too much, suck it up, know that this is what you wanted. If adjustments need to be made, save the conversation for your days off. DO NOT CROSS LINES.

To the cuckoldress, always feel confident in expecting all your needs to be met, even at the expense of your cuckold going without. You will struggle at first. Taking the time and money to get that pampered massage will feel like you're doing something wrong. It goes against the grain of how you've been taught growing up. Cuck's worship selfishness in a cuckold marriage. The more you do it, the better you both feel. Push past the feeling that it's just not proper. If you think you've gone too far, do it anyway and then discuss it on off days.

For both of you, try to leave issues in the vault until you are outside of the cuckold dynamics on your designated days. That's why we have one day a week to go back to L.B.C. (Life Before Cuckolding). The time spent during your cuck cycle should remain sacred for both of you. It is the real you, outwardly being expressed. Most of the issues you both experience are simply growing pains. As you develop, this becomes easier and less frequent.

Chapter Six

HAIR BLOWS

I don't have a chapter's worth to say on this BUT it is of such huge importance; I wanted to make sure it had its designated section.

Hair.

Any and all of the hair on the cuckold belongs to you the cuckoldress. It surprises me how much men care about their hair as much as women do. It forms part of their identity. As a cuckold, they lose that privilege.

If he is going gray, and you want to have him color his head, so be it. You prefer he grows it long or shaves it bald, it's all your call. Forcing him to lose control of his own style is a means of outward control. He may object, but listen ONLY if it's an objection brought forth in off times.

Cuckold men, by the time you reach this point in your cuckold relationship, you don't need to be told. You know. You are not the real alpha man your cuckoldress needs and wants sexually. The fact that you admit it to yourself and allow your goddess to grow and blossom, enjoying the true power and freedom she so greatly deserves, is awesome. Your wife is lucky to have you. Remember, there is nothing wrong with you. Society says you have to be a certain way, but society also said the world was flat at one point.

Now show your cuckoldress the respect she deserves and shave your pubic area. I don't mean clean-up or trim. I mean shave. Bald. Smooth like a little boy. Visually it will help her understand you are a little boy and not a man. It will help you feel like less of a man sexually.

For me, this was a non-negotiable with davie. He did not want to shave, but I will not please him in any way if he is anything less than clean-shaven down there. It's about respect. It's about the one part of the body that is all about sexuality. He is a cuckold, and his sexual anatomy needs to look the part.

Conversely, for the cuckoldresses, I strongly encourage you to practice no kind of personal grooming for your cuck. That's for your bulls to enjoy. If cucky gets to see you clean, it's because you've done so for a bull earlier that day.

Chapter Seven

THE MENTOR

*a*rguably the last step a cuckold couple will take that would not be considered risky, permanent or 'extreme' is getting or becoming a mentor to other cuckold couples.

Finally, being able to talk to other people openly and honestly is incredibly freeing. Early in our exploration, davie and I met a couple (Chloe and Stephen) in a swingers' club. I could not handle seeing davie with another woman, and he had no desire to be with anyone else but me. After many drinks and an after-hours cafe, Chloe suggested we look at cuckolding. Many conversations later, they put us on the right path.

Davie knew he wanted me to be with other men, to be selfish, controlling and to humiliate him. But he also felt like he was broken and went in and out of depression for several months. It was Stephen (Chloe calls him her little stevie) that helped davie understand there was nothing wrong with him. This couple is a large part of how and why we got things right early on. We remain best friends to this day.

When you help other new couples, it affirms your love of this life, your grasp on it and your devotion to it. Helping others helps you. I should take a quick moment to mention I have a private/ "secret" Facebook group (you cannot find it except through the link at the back of this book) that I have created for this purpose. I encourage you to join and share/ask away.

Having a mentor is not just beneficial to help in the initial stages of this lifestyle. As you advance and get more comfortable, it can still be very isolating. The only person you can openly discuss issues or ideas with is your significant other. Mentors not only help to hash things out, they usually become friends you can connect with.

This section started with saying it's the last step. If you connect with people that are more advanced in the lifestyle than yourselves, they will help propel both of you into untapped areas of your sexuality and your darker side. I love love love when davie and I come across a couple that says they are bored. Boy, are they in for a surprise.

Mentors help as a sounding board, as a source of comfort and as friends. But if they are a truly experienced cuckold couple, they will keep reminding you. Cuckolding is not just about sex. It is a way of life that places the females' sexuality as supreme. But it's also about extending her sexual satisfaction and the cuckold's denial of sexual satisfaction. Disparity, humiliation, control and unconditional acceptance and love. In a nutshell, this is cuckolding.

It becomes easy to forget much of this. A mentor

should not only constantly remind you, but they should also encourage you. Cuckold mentors provide comfort when your cucky is going through angst. You would think they get used to it, but they don't. Having another cuck to tell them it's okay takes that emotional stress away. A cuckoldress mentor ideally should become a partner in crime. They should help you ignore feelings of guilt and encourage ways for you to expand your selfish side.

Yes, it sounds like a convoluted cluster of nonsense. To the outside vanilla world, I suppose it is. Cuckolding is not part of normal society. We are a group of men and women that have come to terms with a side of us that is shunned in regular life. Sticking together, supporting each other and offering an ear is something this community so desperately needs. If you don't have a mentor or you are not being a mentor, do it. Do it now.

Chapter Eight

WHOSE MONEY IS IT?

☙

his is where things get interesting. If you are here, you are in a truly committed cuckold marriage. You have crossed so many social barriers and now you want your cake and want to eat it too. Traveling this path is irreversible, and I caution all readers. These 'steps'/suggestions are assuming you have no recurring issues with the lifestyle up to this point. You're both happier and more satisfied with how things have progressed and are now looking to go all the way.

Full disclosure.

Davie and I have been in this space for just over 2 years at the time of this writing. It took 5 years as a cuckold couple before we were comfortable taking some of these steps. Some of these actions we have not done ourselves, but we know other couples that enjoy and appreciate them. Every couple is different. Do what works for you as a couple. Just beware, these actions can bring your marriage very close to the edge. In part, why they are so tempting. Cuckolding is about pushing the envelope. With that said,

Money. Who makes it? Who controls it? Who has access to it?

The answer to all of these should be obvious. If little cucky has one soft place (besides his little pee pee) it's his wallet. This needs to be eradicated as much as humanly possible. He should have zero access to any household income, WITHOUT your knowledge and expressed approval under any circumstances.

The steps are easy. Open a bank account in your name only (cuckoldress), contact your employer (bank, if your self employed) to notify them of a change in your direct deposit (cuckold). All money he makes goes to this new account set up in your name only. Remove all existing money from any shared accounts you have. Provide him with an agreed monthly allowance that you deposit into the old joint account to which he has access. And you're done.

The upside? The cuckoldresss is now in complete and total control of the entire cash flow. Cucky has no access to withdrawal or even enquire on how much, where, when, or why. You completely cut him out of the financial loop. This is true dominance and control. You have money to do as you see fit, no questions asked.

The downside? If you mismanage the finances, you could be solely responsible for some serious financial crises. Additionally, being the sole person with access to funds, you're responsible for making sure all the household bills are paid timely.

The whole point of doing all this is not to encourage

any cuckoldress to become financially reckless. It's giving you total control monetarily and sexually. This is the mother load. You literally now own your husband cucky. He knows it. You feel it. As long as you make sure it's not in a negative cash flow, it's all good.

At the very beginning of this series (4 books ago) I tried to explain that true cuckolding is the culmination of many other 'kink' activities/lifestyles, all rolled up into one. It is the mother of all kinks. The money side just discussed is separately categorized as 'Findom' (Financial Domination). The difference here is it's not about trying to get all the guy's money. It's about creating a life of unequal. Of humiliation. Of sadism. The list goes on.

I believe cuckolding is the most comprehensive and all-encompassing paradigm of any life two people can voluntarily choose to be a part of, full stop. Seriously. It is because of its far-reaching complexity and that it touches our souls like nothing else. I have never met a couple that has not acknowledged its extremely addictive properties.

If you're serious, money has to go to the cuckoldress. It's just that simple.

Chapter Nine

YOU LOOK SO CUTE IN THOSE PANTIES

⚬

The urban dictionary would call this 'sissification'. The feminization of your husband to look and/or act more girly. How far you go with this is like opening a bag of whoopass. It is a truly personal decision each couple needs to discuss and explore on their own.

What I can tell you is why and how.

Cuckolds reading this will probably blush. Yes, you little girl, I can see you! Cuckoldresses you're thinking wtf? I know I did when davie and I watched some cuckold porn together many years ago. For us, it's not really a thing. I call him my little princess often, but that's about as far as we take things. I am a sadist. I enjoy inflicting uncomfortable and controlling situations on davie. I do not get excited seeing him look like a chick. That being said, I also got breast enlargements to catch the eyes of other men. Some women would view this as too much. No judgment. We are all right.

The point of sissifying your cuckold is to take another step in removing any sense of manhood. It's a perfect form of humiliation that no one can deny. Take a photo of him in your thongs, wearing make-up, pantyhose, and high heels. Just having that image is humiliating. Use it to threaten him being exposed (ONLY AS A MIND GAME) will cause many cucks to ejaculate on the spot. It's one, two, three punches to the cuck's mind. Emasculated, humiliated, and controlled all in one action.

I have a few cuckoldress friends that do this often. One of them has told me she has removed all his underwear completely. He only has a drawer filled with lace and silk women's panties. Yup. Underneath his power suit pants are some sweet and sexy female undergarments. She says he has at least three pairs a week that come home with pre-cum stains on them. She loves the idea of her husband being her best girlfriend. The more girly he is, the better.

I get it. It does kind of appeal to me if I'm to be honest. The idea of finishing off davie in any capacity of being a man is seductive. But for me, I still want my cucky to be my main squeeze. He is my cuck, but he is also my husband. The man that will unconditionally love and protect me. Something tells me that going down that path may jeopardize my feelings towards him. If he ever expressed that he's into it, I'll be all over it like white on rice. It's not a thing for us as it stands.

For those of you that it is a thing, enjoy. For the cuckolds out there, be careful you don't request this kind of treatment without knowing it may change how your cuckoldress views you as a man. It can become a wormhole of emotional separation between you. This is NOT the end goal for any actions either of you does. If it pushes an emotional wedge between, take a hard pass. If it's something you both like and get excited about, go for it!

Chapter Ten

INK DON'T STINK

*T*here are only a few things in life that are considered permanently fixed outcomes. Death and taxes. No matter what you do, you can not avoid these two. I would suggest the next closest thing to these two is tattoos. Okay, yes you can get a tattoo removed but not without significant pain, time, and money. Getting a tattoo is commonly accepted as a permanent installation.

There is something about those who commit to a life-long mark on their body that they have voluntarily chosen and placed. It says something bigger than the tattoo. It says it commits them to whatever that tattoo says/repre-sents/depicts forever and ever amen.

Do you see where I'm going with this? Cuck's, ask yourself how you would feel about your goddess having a tattoo of an ink chain around her ankle with the word "available" or "Hotwife" or "Goddess"? Getting a little hard are we? Cuckoldresses, think of the complete power and control and constant reminder you have for yourself if your little cucky boy has a tattoo directly below his belly button saying "Owned by ___" or "Broken" (with an arrow pointing down to his cock) or having your cucky get a tramp stamp near his tail bone that says "I AM A CUCKOLD".

My point to both of you is it shows a commitment that is permanent and unconditional. This has a tremendous amount of symbolic power, more than most appreciate. Think about the wedding ring. It's not just a ring. It represents a lifelong commitment to another human being.

Having a tattoo is both an inward and outward way of telling yourself, your partner, and the world that cuckolding is who you are, not just what you do. It provides a fixed point of vulnerability with your spouse. Should your marriage ever struggle or even worse, end, it would take a heck of a lot of explaining to the next partner you date. It's a sort of symbolic insurance policy to ensure that kind of uncomfortable situation never arises.

Depending on what and where it can also act as a lifelong point of humiliation to the cuckold. I wonder how davie explains his little billboard when he goes for his annual physical. I do not have any tattoos for no reason other than I have a thing for needles and pain. Not a delightful combination when getting inked.

In a different direction but on the same lines of permanency, let's talk circumcision. For those of you who are already clipped, skip the balance of this chapter and move on. To the unkempt, uncut aardvarks, this is for you.

If you live in most parts of the world outside of North America, circumcision is not the norm. It's a cultural thing. A decision made by your parents that you had no say on. Now you're all grown up and you're a big boy, wearing big boy pants. Yet you have a cock that looks like a headless horseman. I don't care who you are or where you live, an uncut cock is just plain hideous to look at. It has no cosmetic appeal whatsoever.

Cuckoldresses, you may feel indifferent seeing as your primary source of penis pleasure will now come from your bulls. That being said, chances are you are still pleasing your cucky when he's been a good little boy. I think you should not have to look at anything that displeases you. If you want your cuck snipped, have him get it done.

Another overlooked benefit to a circumcised cock is hygiene, especially when a cock cage is on. With a cage on, cucky will have difficulty pulling back his foreskin. If he goes to take a pee with his cage on, a small amount of moisture will be trapped under his foreskin. After a couple of days, this can smell and a buildup of bacteria may cause infection. The only way to prevent this is to have him remove the cage every time he showers (which means you must monitor him so he does not get tempted to please himself) OR you get him cut. As far as I'm concerned, this is a no brainer. All cuckolds need to be snipped. When davie and I first started dating, he was uncircumcised. I had that fixed BEFORE we even discovered cuckolding. I think it looks disgusting.

Chapter Eleven

CLEAN UP DUTY

❧

*N*o, I'm not referring to household chores (See Chapter - "Is My Dinner Ready"). Perhaps this is the most contentious aspect of cuckoldry. Most couples have powerful feelings about this. Many love it and see it as an essential part of the lifestyle. Others vehemently object to the idea, seeing it as a concept largely placed by the porn industry.

On the off chance you've been living under a rock, clean-up in a cuckold context is getting your cuckold to orally please you immediately after you have fucked one of your bulls without the use of a condom. Yes, you read correctly. The result is your cuck ultimately is licking up both your excitement and that of the bull.

This approaches the ultimate act of degradation, humiliation, and control. I get it. For a lot of cuckolds the idea of their goddess demanding they clean-up, it's the pot of gold at the end of the rainbow. Similarly, for many cuckoldresses, having your cucky lick you dry after you've just been fucked hard by a real man... it's the ultimate act of unconditional support your cuck could give you. It will instantly remove any feelings of guilt you may have, especially if your cuck is enjoying it.

There are two fundamental concerns I have with this. Not using a condom and crossing a hard line that could be catastrophic to your marriage.

Having no condom and having a bull fully ejaculate inside you is no longer a representative way of someone 'claiming' you. They are placing genetic material inside you that can create a new life. Yes, I know, that's another level of cuckolding which we will discuss later. The point, exchange of bodily fluids makes it final, the real deal as real as it can get. For that reason, I love it.

But the stakes are very high. Assuming you don't want to get pregnant and assuming you are also using an additional layer of birth control ('the pill' for example), you could still get pregnant. The odds are low, but they are real.

Also, there is an obvious increased risk for sexually transmitted diseases of any kind. We know this lifestyle for having many sexual partners (both the cuckoldress and the bull). Every time you have sex without a condom, that risk goes up. If you both want to play without the use of a condom, I strongly encourage you to keep it to a minimum number of bulls you know and trust.

The second fundamental concern I have is the potential for catastrophic backlash. Most cuckold couples seem split on this issue. One person wants it, the other does not. You rarely see both cuck and cuckoldress on the same page. Unless there is complete desire (not just agreement) this is not a line I would cross. There are just too many things that can go wrong.

I have never asked davie to clean-up a bull's cum. Davie is very vocal that he does not do the guy/gay thing at any level. I understand and respect that. However, I ALWAYS have davie clean up when my bull has worn a condom. I do like to see him submit to me in such a deep way. I should also add, I play with two of my regular bulls without using a condom. I love the feeling of being 'violated', knowing davie is about to climax before I do. Yes, as long as I don't ask him to clean up, he loves it too.

Chapter Twelve

HERE, SUCK THIS HONEY

his is where cuckolding crosses lines that may have nothing to do with cuckolding. It's where I believe things go in an unhealthy direction. However, as the saying goes, different strokes for different folks. If it works for you as a couple and it makes you both happy, that's all that matters. So what exactly am I talking about here? Latent homosexuality and pregnancy. Let's explore the latter first.

Cuckolding is routed in the behavior of the cuckoo bird. It often leaves its eggs in another bird's nest, leaving the responsibility of caring for the baby bird to an unrelated bird. In our context, the idea of having a bull sexually penetrate and satisfy another man's wife usually suffices to meet that bill. However, some want to take this one step further. The bull gets the cuckoldress pregnant, leaving the child-rearing up to the cuckold. This is huge! Bringing a child into this world is a lifelong commitment, physically, emotionally, and financially. This kind of extreme form of cuckolding I believe is what has given cuckolding a bad rap. Intellectually, I think most of us in the lifestyle can appreciate it, but taking things this far is, in my opinion, irresponsible. It's a fantasy that should remain a fantasy. Bringing a child into this world should NOT be a means to satisfy your sexual desires. If you feel compelled to go this far and are certain it will not compromise the life of the child, do it. I think it crosses the ethical line of life and I can not get behind it. I'm just mentioning it because it exists for a tiny segment of cuckold couples.

Latent homosexuality is the other hyper extreme direction cuckolding caters to. This is very prevalent in much of cuckold porn and erotica. This would be the point where your cucky now becomes involved in the sexual play you're having with your bull. Not with you. With the bull. To all you cuckolds reading this, you know who you are.

There are two lines of thought on this activity. The more common is that cuckolds are, at some level, gay or at the very least bi-sexual. The cuckold dynamic strips them of most of their manhood. Having a bull that demands the cuck 'please' him or even better, his cuckoldress commands him to help get the bull hard, it relinquishes the cuck from acknowledging his homosexual side. It's not their choice, right? This has some validity, but only to a point.

Davie is as straight as a ruler. NO MATTER WHAT, he would not help fluff my bull. I tried it once, just to see if I could get him to do what I say, even knowing it was a line not to be crossed. That was the single biggest mistake I have ever made since becoming a cuckold couple. It nearly put an end to our marriage. It took us the better part of a year to regroup and reconcile. I crossed the line because I became intoxicated with the omnipotent power and control I was slowly gaining on my little davie.

Now, if davie was a willing player, I would have had him sucking dicks from that point on. I also know I would have seen my husband in a different light. Not as a man. Not as a little boy. But as a sex partner, that's my best friend. Notice the shift from husband to a friend. Cuck's, you need to understand that this is a one-way street. If your goddess stops seeing you as a life partner (husband) and only sees you as a cuck (sex buddy) your marriage could be in danger. If either of you is interested in following this path, do not do so without having a very open and direct conversation. Cuckoldresses, if you feel compelled to debase your cuck to this level, that's fine. Just be aware of how you will feel about him down the road. Cucks, if you are not open to any man love, make it crystal clear, upfront, and before you're compromised. During playtime, you're in sexual subspace and vulnerable to doing things you will later bitterly resent.

Chapter Thirteen

COMMUNICATION BREAK-DOWN

*I*f you have been a cuckold couple for any proper length of time, you will both appreciate it is like getting a peek into heaven. But it also takes a lot of time, patience, and understanding. The newness will fade and you will both establish routines that help make your lifestyle work for you. This life can be ridiculously busy, especially if you both work full-time jobs, have kids, and a social life that goes beyond cuckolding.

Cuckolding is also a huge emotional roller coaster. You will both have days where you feel high on life, and then days where you're having doubts, guilt, maybe even a massive identity crisis. As time progresses, there is a natural tendency for both partners to become somewhat emotionally desensitized to their partner and his/her needs.

As you grow in this kind of relationship, you both gain more and more confidence to go deeper. Cucky was first happy seeing you screw another man at one point. Now cucky craves being told he's getting locked up for two weeks and you're going to have 2 bulls over on the weekend. Cuckoldress was ecstatic to feel the freedom of having choices in sexual partners beyond hubby. Now she loves the power to demand cucky to do her laundry and make dinner before she comes home from work and a quickie with her favorite bull at a hotel.

All this leads to both of you becoming emotionally disconnected from each other and to a lesser extent yourself. I have said this many times, but I don't believe I can overstate it. You need to have designated 'days off' from the cuckold life. These days should represent an opportunity to have no cuck and goddess. You are wife and husband. No power play. No mind fuck. Nothing but the two of you as a vanilla couple. During these days, you need to give each other ample opportunity to freely speak your mind, express your concerns and suggest modifications.

As you become more experienced, these designated days can happen less frequently and perhaps fall into an unscheduled pattern. The key in all of this is open, honest, raw dialogue. You started this journey that way. It can never be lost or neglected.

The busy bee cuckold will always try to please his goddess. He'll always be doing everything asked of him and then some. He wants nothing more than to serve and worship. The demanding, selfish and mildly devilish cuckoldress feels really comfortable being spoiled, having everything done for her, and always getting her way with little or no challenges. This is great until it's not.

More than any other kind of marriage, cuckold marriages are the closest and most deeply connected. That is not because you have a personal slave or because you have a smokin' hot sexy bitch. It's because this life demands you talk. No filters. No garbage. You both have so much at stake. Don't forget to keep the lines of communication open and on at all times. If you lose this openness, a hard reset needs to happen fast.

Stop, drop, and roll

Leave the cuckold life. Rediscover each other as lovers in love. Remember, cuckolding was something you both entered to enhance your lives together. To give you both an opportunity to let your inner self out and to be loved and accepted despite its ugliness. Cuckolding should never work except to draw you closer together, to deepen your love, and to enhance your lives.

Don't worry about re-entering the life. You will. You both don't get this far and do not recognize there is something cuckolding offers that is magical, euphoric, and addictive. Just make sure you do not go back until your back on the same page emotionally, mentally, and physically.

Chapter Fourteen

DISPARITY OVER-LOAD

∽♂∽

*D*isparity over-loading. It's not a question of will it happen to you as a couple. It's a matter of when and by how much.

Cuckolding is built around disparity/unfairness/a flagrant disregard for balance in a relationship. In the bedroom, the kitchen, the bank account. EVERY-WHERE. As you progress down the cuckolding life, eventually this lack of balance will become skewed too much in the one direction.

The natural inclination is to assume that the cuckold is delegated too many chores or is asked to suffer too long with a cock cage on or is left sitting at home too many times while his goddess is out playing with a bull. This can and usually happens at some point. You both need to learn an alternative way of living with rules that contradict social norms completely. You can easily adjust this with little effort. Next designated off day, you as the cuckold should show your feelings of being overwhelmed, over deprived, or over worked. What many cuckolds couples cannot recognize are the other three ways that disparity can be abused or misused.

The flip side of a cuckold being too imbalanced is feeling like there is not enough of an imbalance. Things seem too fair and equal to the cuckold. This is often the case in newer cuckold relationships where the cuckoldress struggles to let go of the fairness lessons taught in grade school. She will grapple with feeling like a mean or a bad person if... This is where massive growth happens as you both come to terms with the sadistic or masochistic side of yourselves. As a cuckoldress grows and develops, you learn to stop feeling apologetic or bad for being selfish. HOWEVER, if this situation of being too equal continues deep into your cuckolding relationship, your cuck may feel more pain and emptiness than if you were flat out cruel and unfair. He craves this. It's the upside-down world, remember? Your acts of unfairness are, in effect, acts of kindness and love.

The other two kinds of mismanaged disparity, to the best of my knowledge, are never acknowledged or discussed. Disparity issues the cuckoldress struggles with. Has anyone considered the possibility that the cuckoldress feels empty or less fulfilled, BECAUSE she is contributing little to nothing to the household? This is one that I have heard from other cuckoldresses a lot. Giving to their husband (not cuckold) makes them feel whole. Turning that tap off can cause some emotional ripples to the mind. Usually, it's just a matter of getting used to being a goddess. If you continue to feel this way after a sustained period, perhaps dialing back the level of disparity is needed. You both need to constantly tweak what is the ideal balance, or in this case, imbalance.

The final trouble area of disparity is the cuckoldress not making things unfair enough. She feels less than a goddess. She makes efforts to impose inequality, only to be met by a reluctant cuckold that does not want to do the time or the work. This is the worst-case scenario and needs to be looked at with surgical gloves on.

Chances are extremely good, cucky boy was the one to bring the entire lifestyle to your attention. He started the entire conversation and journey. His lack of willingness to worship you in any way says one of two things. Either he is reneging on the desire to truly be a cuckold OR you are being used to fulfill his little sex fantasy and now he's bored? If he wants out, that needs addressing right away. Things will get sticky if it's not brought to the table. If this is just a fantasy thing for him and not for you, you could look at hotwifing as a direction to take things. However, if you're a true cuckoldress, that will not satisfy your hunger for power, control, and disparity.

I'd recommend seeking marriage counseling at that point. You have bared your soul to this man. He has essentially used you as a sex toy. Not cool. This is why I spent so much time in the previous two books dedicated to each partner individually(husband/wife) so this kind of situation could be avoided.

Chapter Fifteen

BUT I LOVE HIM

*P*ossibly the absolute worst thing that can happen in a cuckold marriage. It is the cuckold's worst fear coming to fruition. It is one of the major reasons the cuckoldress is reluctant to entire the lifestyle. They both do everything to avoid this and yet, it sometimes happens. The cuckoldress (wife) becomes emotionally attached to one of her bulls and 'falls in love with the bull' and usually out of love with her cuck (husband).

This is catastrophic and should theoretically never happen. It rarely happens, but it sometimes does. The human emotional condition is complex and constantly changing. I have never met any cuckold couples where this has been the case, but I have heard of a few cases where it has happened. I want to reassure all readers, this is rare and can easily be avoided but can just as easily happen if you don't keep your love relationship vibrant and growing.

Why does it happen? Two words. Honesty (with your

partner AND yourself) and communication (with your partner and your bull).

Sexuality and love are very separate and distinct aspects of any relationship. In the vanilla world, they are always mashed together as one element. In a cuckold relationship, they are as separate as could be. However, living most of your life where the two elements are slammed together, it can be a simple thing to mix up.

Day after day, month after month, year after year, as a cuckold couple you may grow emotionally apart as sex becomes more about a third person and less about the two of you as a couple. The sex between you becomes more of a mind fuck and less about the physical act. I'm not suggesting you don't have some physical sexual contact, but the point is disparity. The intensity of sexual encounters between you will be intensified dramatically but at a significantly reduced frequency. This is a natural evolution of any cuckold marriage.

Now enter bull number one, two, three, or whatever. They are having regular, ongoing sex with the cuckoldress. There is a regular exchange of high energy sex, attention, caressing, and pleasure. You do not have to be a rocket scientist to do the math. Left unchecked for extended periods, this bull/cuckoldress relationship may cross the sex barrier into the emotional world.

All this can be avoided easily. The problem is not avoidance. Does the genuine concern happen if it's too late?

Here we go again. The easiest way to ensure this kind of situation never arises is by having scheduled 'off days'. This allows both the cuck and the cuckoldress an opportunity to express fears, concerns or even bring attention to the other person things they are sensing or witnessing that the other person may be unaware of. For the cuckoldress, you may notice or sense your cuck is overly and unjustifiably worried about your attachment to a specific bull. Yes, you want your cuck to feel jealous but not concerned that he's going to lose you as his loyal, loving wife. To the cuck, you may see your cuckoldress gets all googly-eyed or constantly talking fondly about a specific bull. The implication being she has drawn an emotional connection to the bull beyond being amazing in bed. Both of you need to watch each other's backs. It's all fun and games until your marriage is a mess.

The next most obvious way to avoid building an emotional connection to a bull is regularity. If you only see a bull a few times a year, it becomes almost impossible to feel anything besides his huge, hard cock. If he is that good that you want to see him frequently, make sure you both monitor the risks in real-time. Also, as a cuckoldress, if you ever begin to feel an emotional connection that transcends the sexual energy of your bull, pull the pin. Stop seeing that bull, period. Don't tempt yourself with emotional quicksand. Once you get sucked into an emotional hole, it becomes a million times harder for both you and your cuck to recover.

One other point I feel should be brought to everyone's attention. As cuckolding has grown in public awareness and popularity, so has the number of single men ready, willing, and able to act like the bull. Sadly, many of the new bull generation are not real bulls. They do not understand the true dynamics of cuckolding. They fail to recognize or understand cuckolding is not a lack of love between a husband and wife. It's an overabundance of love, respect, and giving. These 'bulls' (I put this in quotes because this group are not bulls, they are predators) see the whole cuckold lifestyle as a joke. They take pride in doing whatever they can to destroy your marriage. They will try to proactively get in the cuckoldresses' head and heart. They will often disrespect the cuck in an unwelcome way. Their end game is to get off, and if they destroy your marriage, that's a bonus to their ego. If you ever have the misfortune of being with this kind of bull (I call them rams, davie calls them fuckhead's) run fast and run far. Do not engage at any level or under any circumstances. They are the single biggest threat to the entire cuckold life.

Finally, what do you do if it's too late? If you have fallen in love with your bull or if your cuckoldress says she no longer loves you. This is the darkest side of cuckolding. I don't know of one couple that has navigated through this and has survived. From my experience, I would say it's a terminal situation. I know this is not the solution you want to hear. The lesson to take from this is DO NOT let things ever get to this point. Always love each other and remember the bull is a toy to your marriage. He is nothing else.

Chapter Sixteen

WHAT WILL THE NEIGHBORS THINK

oday, right now, do you have any idea what your sister is having for dinner? Do you know where the car is going that just drove past your house? Do you have any idea what your best friend at work does when she wants to get her husband all turned on? Chances are, you do not know AND you don't care. Welcome to the reality of humanity. Everyone is so wrapped up in their own little worlds, the day-to-day activities of random strangers or even people close to them are irrelevant.

Cuckolding is a monumental shift from the vanilla world, I'll grant you that. But, how many people like to go to the bathroom and vomit after dinner? How many people pick their nose while they're driving? What about drugs and alcohol? Do you think every single person you know has no chemical dependencies on anything? Chances are most people do something that is totally uncool by society's standards. We all just don't talk about it or are unaware of it. Cuckolding is no different.

It has been around since sexuality was around. It is way waaaaaaay more common as a fantasy than almost anyone would care to admit. Number 2 search word according to Pornhub (the largest on-line porn site on the internet) is cuckolding. That's A LOT of people.

My point, if you're even a little concerned about being outed by others, it's just not going to happen, unless you want it to. Be discreet. Only share your life with others in the life and if anyone asks, lie. IT'S NONE OF THEIR FUCKING BUSINESS! Do you ask your brother if he masturbates when he's in the bathroom? Do you ask your colleague if they need to use lubrication during sex because they have issues with menopause? If someone asks, in my mind they've already crossed a line that only deserves an equal response of lacking respect. Lie!

That all said, your children are a wholly unique situation. You live with them, and this will cause some awkward situations if things are not handled properly. I want to say up front; I am not suggesting you tell your children about your sex life. It's none of their business either. What goes on behind your bedroom door is for you as a couple and no one else. What does need to be addressed is the stuff that goes on outside the bedroom. The 'why is daddy always doing all the work?' Or 'how come mommy is always out with her friend Billy?'.

They live with you, and they will see your dynamics differ from their friend's parents. Same as with your friends, where applicable, lie. I assure you, your kids are unlikely to tell you they are about to go over to their friend's house to have sex, even if it is very much their plan. Some things are just not to be discussed with your kids.

The disparity that lives outside the bedroom is however I believe an awesome life teaching experience. Davie and I have two children, a boy, and a girl. They are now both in their late teens and very much have a life outside of mom and dad. They do not know that we are a cuckold couple. They do however know that we are in a female-led relationship. Mom is the boss. Dad is a loyal, loving partner that does everything he can to make his wife happy. That's all they know. That's all they need to know.

We have both been very vocal in promoting an FLR relationship to both our kids. Do I want my kids to follow in our footsteps? As for cuckolding, I couldn't care less. As for living an FLR, absolutely! My son has so much more respect for girls than any of his peers. I thank davie for that. My daughter understands she does not need to be second, the invisible, supportive partner in any relationship she takes on. She is a strong, vibrant young lady that will take the world by storm.

I think these are good values to instill in our kids. The old school mentality of the sexist, semi misogynistic man with the timid, selfless and low self-confidence woman is dead. I do not want my kids entering the adult world with anything less than a healthy respect for both genders. Our cuckolding relationship is private. The fact that davie is respectful and attentive to me and I am a confident force is public.

Chapter Seventeen

IS THAT BOB AND SOPHIA OVER THERE?

this was one of my biggest concerns when davie and I started our journey into alternative sex activities. When I think about it now, it's almost laughable but, I appreciate it can be an actual concern to the point of stopping some couples in their tracks.

We did not start our marriage out as a cuckold couple. We were as vanilla as they come. Our idea of a sexcapade was for me to say a naughty word or for davie to give me a little spank while we were 'making love'. I could tell he wanted more, but I did not know what it was. Perhaps some sexy lingerie? That worked, but only as much as turning a single night light off saves on your electrical bill.

I asked if there was anything we could do to spice our sex life up. Davie started talking about swinging and checking out a sex club in our local area. We were just going to check it out, right? I could not deal to see davie with another woman, so I made him swear we were only going to see what's out there.

Three weeks went by before we finally got the courage to go to their 'newbie/orientation' night. It was a one-hour tour of the place and a quick review of the club rules before the club opened to its regular members. Curiosity alone made us both agree to stay and wait till the club was open.

By the end of the night, we saw things that neither of us had ever thought possible. Group orgies, threesomes, random hand jobs on the dance floor with everyone showing nothing but praise and encouragement. It was bizarre and erotic. By the time we got home, we were both so horny; the sex was animalistic.

Another couple of weeks went by before we went again. It seemed the exposure to such open sexuality did something to both our heads. Until this point, it was just a fun exploration of a different world. We did nothing ourselves other than watch with open mouths.

Then it hit me.

What if we see anyone there we know? I mean, Oh My God! I would be embarrassed and mortified if I saw a friend or someone either of us knew from work. I panicked and insisted davie turn the car around. This was too high a risk. If someone saw us at a sex club (keep in mind, we still had not even talked about cuckolding at this point), I would want to crawl in a hole and die.

Davie calmed me down and made me quickly realize, if they see me, I see them as well. If we are both at a swingers sex club, oh well. I know it seems like common sense, but I just didn't see it that way.

I wanted to add this as a footnote chapter for those of

you that have made your journey intellectually, you just haven't left the house. Do not let your vanity and any over-concern about what others will think to stop you from this wonderful journey. Believe me, everyone has their dirty little secrets. You don't need to broadcast that you are a cuckold couple, but meeting other couples that you know are actively involved in any sexual adventures outside vanilla is not a bad thing. Remaining silent is mutually understood by everyone.

CUCKOLDING IS THE BEGINNING

*I*f you have made it this far, I suspect you have already started a path into cuckolding as a couple. I have tried to create a series of books that, cumulatively, will help both of you feel confident and aware of this life. I have also tried to balance the equation so you're not misinformed or misguided to believe it's for anyone/everyone. It is not!

I'm not suggesting there are any rules, regulations, or a rule book stipulating what is a prerequisite to calling yourselves a cuckold couple. Many couples enjoy the sexual energy and dynamics of hotwifing - cuckolding without the elements outside the bedroom.

For davie and I, hotwifing is too limiting and does not allow both of us to explore and expand our real personal needs. Hotwifing is rather single-dimensional and is just about the sex. Not saying there is anything wrong with it. It can be amazing for many couples, and that's all they want. Cuckolding in its comprehensive format is a much deeper and rewarding experience.

Both of us are always having sex. Mind sex. 24/7. Cuckolding is all about the headspace, the control, the humiliation, and the mutual acceptance of our inner cores. I am the boss. Period. Davie is my cucky. This is regardless of being at a hotel with a bull, going to a sex club, going grocery shopping, or going on a vacation.

We are a cuckold couple that runs as a female-led relationship. All traditional cuckold relationships (that means 100%) either start as a female-led relationship or they end as being one.

As much as cuckolding allows both partners to explore their darkest sides, it ultimately circles back to one key element. The wife is a goddess. She is the center of the relationship. Her happiness and satisfaction are the beginning, middle, and end. With this prime directive, the cuck derives his true purpose in life. To ensure her happiness, unconditionally, at all times.

I dare you to find a single successful cuckold couple that would ever go back to anything vanilla. It does not work for many. But boy does it work for those that have the right DNA.

Finally, I thank you for reading my series. I have tried to be as comprehensive as possible. I'm new to this writing thing so, if I've glossed over areas you want more information on, I have set up a private (not discoverable using any search terms) Facebook group for cuckold couples. It will give us all a safe and supportive place to talk, share and answer issues that arise. If you're reading this on an ebook, click the Facebook icon in the "about the author" section to be taken directly to the group. If you are reading this in paperback, here is the link: https://www.facebook.com/groups/cuckoldcouples/.

I wish you and your goddess/cuckold nothing but success, happiness, and love. Remember, cuckolding is sex-driven but is ONLY a deeper way to express your true and unconditional love to each other. Never forget that.

Hugs and Kisses

xo

COMING SOON

THE MENTOR 1
A BAD INFLUENCE

Allore Sinclair

FROM HOUSE WIFE TO HOTWIFE

When Anna starts a fitness class to improve her self esteem, she meets the mysterious Julia. This new woman takes her under her wings, suggesting Anna consider a seductive change to her marriage dynamics. Anna's husband, Robert feels the friend is not good for his wife, but also can't help wanting Julia's influence to get stronger. Is Julia an angel or devil in disguise?

ALSO BY ALLORA SINCLAIR

ABOUT THE AUTHOR

Allora Sinclair is a happily married 40 year old. She and her loving cuckold husband Dave (davie) have been in a cuckold marriage for over seven years and she has now decided to start documenting their journey from vanilla to a complete FLR relationship. If Allora is not found at her computer or out shopping for shoes, she is usually found in the caring arms of davie or embraced in ecstasy with one of her favourite bulls. She has done a series of non-fiction books to help couples navigate their way through the heavily distorted life of being a cuckold couple. She is now working on a series of fiction books that are based on some of their real-life experiences. If you like what she's doing, please leave a review wherever you purchased this book.

Made in the USA
Middletown, DE
22 February 2021